15-Minute Language Arts Skill-Builders

Written by Barbara T. Doherty & Charlotte S. Jaffe
Cover Illustrated by Karen Sigler
Text Illustrations by Koryn Agnello & Karen Sigler

ISBN 1-56644-066-1

EDUCATIONAL IMPRESSIONS, INC.
Hawthorne, New Jersey 07507

Printed in the U.S.A.

Contents

Teacher Directions and Overview

Add sparkle and fun to your language arts classroom by using *15-Minute Language Arts Skill-Builders* with your students on a daily or weekly basis. The activity pages are self-directing and can be used in the following ways:

- warm-up activities
- supplementary lessons
- homework assignments
- independent extensions
- cooperative-learning projects
- competitions
- preparation for standardized tests

The book is divided into five skill-builder sections: Synonyms & Antonyms, Using Words Wisely, Determine the Meaning, Sequencing, Fact or Opinion, and Interpreting. The activities challenge students' higher-level thinking and offer teachers an excellent evaluation tool! There is diversity in the degree of difficulty. In general, easier activities are found at the beginning of each section and more difficult ones at the end.

These activities can also be used competitively. Directions for scoring the skill pages as a class or group competition are included on the first page of each activity section.

Barbara T. Doherty
Charlotte S. Jaffe

SECTION I
Synonyms and Antonyms

Suggested Time: 15 minutes
(1 minutes for directions)
(14 minutes for activity)

This section contains both synonym and antonym skill-builder activity pages. Students must select the word that is **most nearly the same** as the key word on the left for the synonym pages and the word that is **most nearly the opposite** as the key word on the left for the antonym pages.

Directions for Use as Self-Directed Activities:
Distribute the materials to the students, who will complete the work independently. As self-directed activities, the sheets are especially useful as warm-up activities, supplementary lessons, homework assignments, and independent extensions.

Directions for Use as Competitive Activities:
Divide the students into teams. Allow one minute to explain the directions and scoring and fourteen minutes for students to complete the activities. The time allotted will vary with the ability level of the class. When the allotted time has expired, or when all the students have completed the sheets, total the number of correct responses. Award one point for each correct answer. Tally each team member's points and record the group's total points on the scoresheet. For example, 14 correct responses = 14 points. If the activity is done as a team effort with members calling out the answers and a member writing them on the chalkboard, the scoring is also one point for each correct answer.

Synonyms and Antonyms: No. 1

Find the word that means **nearly the same** as the word on the left. Put a circle around your answer.

Example:

leap .... start bend run (jump)

1. move .... stay go plan help
2. herd .... group farm listen sound
3. medal .... iron steel mix in award
4. hoarse .... animal clear croaky colt
5. meat .... food encounter agree join
6. plain .... smooth helicopter pretty simple
7. short .... quick tall small early
8. see .... water look lake find
9. shabby .... new sneaky threadbare cheap
10. peal .... load skin ring light
11. sure .... coast beach support certain
12. strange .... familiar unusual uneven lost
13. knew .... old up-to-date modern understood
14. buy .... good-bye near purchase leave
15. study .... subject math learn listen
16. surprised .... shocked expected needed confused
17. hide .... darken seek conceal show
18. help .... control assist block need
19. pupil .... class teacher student boy
20. automobile .... limousine truck bus trailer

Synonyms and Antonyms: No. 2

Find the word that means **nearly the same** as the word on the left. Put a circle around your answer.

Example:

peace .... part keen (calm) restless

1. friend .... neighbor co-worker enemy companion
2. common .... unique imperfect fair ordinary
3. vanish .... escape disappear return trick
4. sensible .... illogical foolish rational smart
5. differ .... disagree disobey disrupt displease
6. ask .... state answer question reply
7. sorrow .... lose apologize sadness pain
8. drowsy .... alert thirsty sleepy dull
9. diminish .... reject increase control lessen
10. get .... lose acquire buy purchase
11. idle .... weak lazy occupied god-like
12. keep .... hide hold release obey
13. meek .... gentle proud bold kind
14. sole .... single shoe vital spirit
15. shiver .... shine tremble wither enfold
16. rare .... common meat scarce frequent
17. modern .... antique near soon present
18. side .... radius center edge inner
19. relate .... question refer pronounce tell
20. scorn .... regard disdain honor betray

Synonyms and Antonyms: No. 3

Find the word that means **nearly the same** as the word on the left. Put a circle around your answer.

Example:

big .... little (large) more hard

1. ancient .... modern used new old
2. beak .... foot glass nose light
3. blend .... melt mix add motion
4. dawn .... morning sunset noon sky
5. kind .... cruel good-hearted happy knowing
6. stubborn .... angry stubby firm impatient
7. just .... neat plain fair difficult
8. worry .... sad secure care need
9. contest .... action victory competition game
10. crafty .... sculptor sly build design
11. frugal .... thrifty wasteful tricky wary
12. ruin .... uncover waste destroy restore
13. amuse .... entertain bore laugh desire
14. lonely .... free plain escorted solitary
15. insert .... extract submerge inside implant
16. revise .... refer release change review
17. confuse .... involve challenge bewilder reveal
18. mystery .... detective puzzle myth confuse
19. agree .... disagree except equal concur
20. loose .... free find fix misplace

Synonyms and Antonyms: No. 4

Find the word that means **nearly the same** as the word on the left. Put a circle around your answer.

Example:

neat .... sparkling (tidy) clean messy

1. brook .... bay stream ocean dam
2. secluded.. hidden promised warned toasted
3. local .... distant afar direct nearby
4. area .... ample enough zone disappear
5. reindeer .... antelope caribou elk white tail
6. crowd .... pair jam banner cruise
7. preserve .... save remote discard destroy
8. cruise .... struggle glide wage fight
9. corn .... grain maize pop oil
10. innocent .... pure tested old worn
11. doctor .... medical intern clinic physician
12. courage .... desert bravery cowardice honesty
13. alert .... warning sleepy trail correct
14. sorcery .... dish skillet magic savory
15. meek .... boisterous mild fresh bring
16. groan .... laugh roar gurgle moan
17. trail .... steep rocky spiral path
18. native .... alien foreign natural pleasing
19. sticky .... slick tacky smooth gum
20. long .... short extensive mile year

Synonyms and Antonyms: No. 5

Find the word that means **nearly the same** as the word on the left. Put a circle around your answer.

Example:

peel .... ring (rind) pelt hide

1. article .... story verb plaza window
2. dare .... agree soar challenge amend
3. floss .... flock thread flue tone
4. answer .... question reply ask libel
5. pungent .... mild sharp dull broil
6. red .... green azure crimson beige
7. lively .... deadly fatal brisk foaming
8. surprise .... overwhelm anticipate remember astonish
9. wood .... lumber could attempt should
10. distant .... close aloof nearly away
11. ripen .... mature young newborn adorable
12. pick .... harden tender lose choose
13. extra .... fine recall surplus perception
14. nearly .... ever beginning almost cunning
15. trio .... partner pair threesome mob
16. erase .... add member void fraction
17. cabinet .... counter table cupboard shelf
18. lawn .... garden turf flower shrub
19. waste .... splurge save thrifty stomach
20. horror .... pretend freeze attract terror

Synonyms and Antonyms: No. 6

Find the word that means **nearly the same** as the word on the left. Put a circle around your answer.

Example:

song .... poem (melody) note piano

1. cloudy.. clear bright windy misty
2. tangy .... bland dreary spicy dull
3. voyage .... yacht trip bridge dance
4. fleck .... stripe speck dot shade
5. question .... answer flower query remote
6. reply .... respond holiday natural crisis
7. dressed .... correct clad willing used
8. puzzle.. pieces cipher solution dilemma
9. sentry .... citizen soldier guard sergeant
10. balmy .... warm happy frosty windy
11. tranquil .... easy free fresh peaceful
12. frigid .... frightening polar cold milky
13. merge.. meet freight appear powerful
14. revolve .... remain begin turn upon
15. racket .... clamor shuttle whirl serve
16. blunder.. astonish mistake bewilder confection
17. haul .... purchase transport booty passageway
18. fantastic .... wonderful awful dreary adventure
19. bold .... pale vivid frantic dire
20. sword .... saber mace knife javelin

Synonyms and Antonyms: No. 7

Find the word that means **nearly the opposite** as the word on the left. Put a circle around your answer.

Example:

subtract .... few more quotient (add)

1. fast .... slow quick lazy easy
2. girl .... man woman boy child
3. light .... small heavy weight fat
4. ceiling .... attic roof wall floor
5. on .... upon into off below
6. clean .... wash dirty tidy disorganized
7. northeast .... southeast northwest midwest southwest
8. push .... pound pull throw shove
9. open .... remove window close stop
10. ride .... walk sit run sail
11. head .... side top foot bottom
12. uncle .... cousin aunt grandfather grandmother
13. busy .... active inactive silent lazy
14. crooked .... neat straight curved bent
15. noisy .... soft loud quiet gentle
16. catch .... take lose throw clutch
17. ebb .... increase move sink wave
18. fable .... novel fact tale fantasy
19. punish .... assist reward correct hurt
20. permit .... damage allow prevent help

Synonyms and Antonyms: No. 8

Find the word that means **nearly the opposite** as the word on the left. Put a circle around your answer.

Example:

top .... floor above (bottom) low

1. strange .... unusual weird extraordinary normal
2. clean .... messy dirty lazy shiny
3. cheerful .... happy clam sad lonely
4. young .... childlike immature old new
5. night .... light star day sun
6. before .... tomorrow after now yesterday
7. first .... second one side last
8. weep .... cry moan laugh absent
9. dull .... new bright clean cheery
10. open .... door close bare available
11. proud .... afraid embarrassed ashamed coward
12. something .... down negative nothing tidy
13. high .... raise above up low
14. long .... year short rope like
15. wide .... long short tidy narrow
16. weary .... tired rested lazy grumpy
17. whole .... entire part all bleak
18. stiff .... rigid flexible rough even
19. equal .... even unbalanced all nothing
20. add .... subtract multiply zero divide

Synonyms and Antonyms: No. 9

Find the word that means **nearly the opposite** as the word on the left. Put a circle around your answer.

Example:

notice .... (overlook) ocean see disappear

1. daring .... bold quiet timid excitable
2. costly .... expensive invaluable cheap small
3. answer .... question apology reply report
4. fame .... glory defeat winner obscurity
5. save .... rescue waste catch loose
6. pupil .... learner principal teacher student
7. climb.. descend mount creep tumble
8. clever .... weak expert ignorant smart
9. near .... separate distant close adjacent
10. win .... overcome defeat lose victory
11. peril .... safety danger hurtful courage
12. hold .... have keep drop break
13. grow .... lose shrink advance end
14. hoarse .... mellow cow rough loud
15. humid .... sunny moist rainy dry
16. front .... face below after rear
17. begin .... finish prepare start behind
18. fresh .... unused old raw new
19. above .... beyond beneath behind before
20. sturdy .... thick firm meek weak

Synonyms and Antonyms: No. 10

Find the word that means **nearly the opposite** as the word on the left. Put a circle around your answer.

Example:

loose.. find relax (tight) gain

1. retreat.. shrink treat advance leave
2. small.. limited change large narrow
3. few .... total some one many
4. hot .... warm cold winter freeze
5. slender .... thin slight short fat
6. victory.. fame reward defeat trounce
7. conceal.. repeat hide show sly
8. bind .... release book tie lose
9. talkative .... vivacious animated laconic verbose
10. drench .... soak dry evaporate moist
11. awkward.. clumsy easy fit graceful
12. rude .... calm pleasant polite nasty
13. smile... grin frown laugh sulk
14. calm .... stormy steady bother quiet
15. wild... loose tame savage unclear
16. believe .... know trust doubt suspect
17. borrow .... take give lend keep
18. stingy .... generous cheap needy free
19. quiet... nosy howl loud talk
20. dull .... light dim blur sharp

Synonyms and Antonyms: No. 11

Find the word that means **nearly the opposite** as the word on the left. Put a circle around your answer.

Example:

plus .... subtract (minus) and add

1. bright .... smart light dull floppy
2. hard .... difficult firm tough easy
3. wet .... moist damp dry warm
4. fail .... quit flunk succeed lack
5. sweet .... sour candy fresh sugary
6. fact .... information lie detail data
7. swell .... grow shrink ripen enlarge
8. re-cycle .... reuse dispose save re-appear
9. meet .... gather scatter join greet
10. ill .... healthy sick unwell doctor
11. courage .... smell graph fable cowardice
12. drafty .... still breezy warm windy
13. bother .... disturb annoy irk ignore
14. fix .... repair destroy amend rebuild
15. old .... ancient aged recent used
16. thrill .... tingle vibrate bore tremble
17. flow .... move stand pour tend
18. surplus .... balanced deficit surpass excess
19. brother .... grandmother sister cousin aunt
20. loose .... disconnected tight free slack

Synonyms and Antonyms: No. 12

Find the word that means **nearly the opposite** as the word on the left. Put a circle around your answer.

Example:

soft .... (hard) smart mushy mild

1. stay .... remain pause halt leave
2. finish .... cease desist end start
3. clear .... transparent bright obscure ensure
4. praise .... encourage criticize commend compliment
5. stop .... prevent defeat end continue
6. clatter .... noise silence rattle commotion
7. common .... ordinary public unusual extra
8. new .... recent modern novel ancient
9. sensible .... foolish trivial unimportant reasonable
10. used .... worn old experienced new
11. fatal .... lifesaving deadly lethal ruinous
12. border .... perimeter boundary center edge
13. amuse .... entertain bore divert pleasant
14. nourish .... sustain prolong support starve
15. serious .... earnest important comic drama
16. royal .... noble kingly common monarch
17. exasperate .... frustrate enrage please praise
18. fuel .... feed firewood coolant fan
19. victor .... loser winner champion vibrant
20. likeable .... charming congenial pleasant menacing

SECTION II
Using Words Wisely

Suggested Time: 15 minutes
(1 minutes for directions)
(14 minutes for competitive activity)

This section contains skill-builder activities in which students are asked to choose the word that **most meaningfully completes** the answer.

Directions for Use as Self-Directed Activities:
Distribute the materials to the students, who will complete the work independently. As self-directed activities, the sheets are especially useful as warm-up activities, supplementary lessons, homework assignments, and independent extensions.

Directions for Use as Competitive Activities:
Divide the students into teams. Allow one minute to explain the directions and scoring and fourteen minutes for students to complete the activities. The time allotted will vary with the ability level of the class. When the allotted time has expired, or when all the students have completed the sheets, total the number of correct responses. Award one point for each correct answer. Tally each team member's points and record the group's total points on the scoresheet. For example, 14 correct responses = 14 points. If the activity is done as a team effort with members calling out the answers and a member writing them on the chalkboard, the scoring is also one point for each correct answer.

Using Words Wisely: No. 1

In each sentence, one word has been omitted. Read each sentence and the words that follow. Circle the word that completes the sentence in the **most meaningful way.**

1. The summer is very ____________ and hot.
   pleasant   sunny   warm   short

2. If you catch a fish, ____________ I will cook it.
   soon   or   then   but

3. Sue is younger than John, ____________ she is taller than he is.
   so   but   and   for

4. He used a rake to ____________ leaves.
   find   stop   get   gather

5. A ____________ has five sides.
   triangle   hexagon   pentagon   octagon

6. Because Ron asks questions, he is thought to be ____________.
   inquisitive   blunt   careful   thoughtful

7. The tennis score was thirty-____________.
   lob   serve   set   love

8. Because his friend was ill, the boy's mood was ____________.
   gleeful   upset   crying   gloomy

9. The sea ____________ caused the sailboat to move quickly.
   water   breeze   waves   weed

10. I am interested in science ____________ I also like math.
    while   since   so   but

11. Joanne looked up the definitions of the words in the ____________.
    encyclopedia   lexicon   Reader's Guide   atlas

12. They sought legal help from their ____________.
    supervisor   attorney   doctor   teacher

Using Words Wisely: No. 1, Cont.

13. The blue whale, threatened with ____________, is on the list of endangered species.

    contamination extinction containment starvation

14. The horticulturist was busily engaged in the study of ____________.

    birds fish flowers stamps

15. Practical jokes that hurt people can be ____________.

    dangerous fake funny incorrect

16. I ____________ the critic's unfair opinion of my new book.

    favored resented shared accepted

17. Since I do not agree with you, I will ____________ your statement.

    answer prove repeat contradict

18. The bright sunlight was ____________ by the opaque window.

    increased dimmed colored unchanged

19. The ____________ set up the museum's art exhibit.

    conductor commander superintendent curator

20. Because he does not spend his money easily, Jim is said to be ____________.

    frugal fastidious fearful fitful

21. His studies of theology helped him to become an able ____________.

    doctor lawyer minister teacher

22. The college students were assigned to live in ____________.

    penthouses dormitories bungalows barracks

23. The heavy rainfall left the ground in a ____________ state.

    misty arid sallow sodden

24. By taking over the boat and refusing to obey the captain, the sailors took part in a ____________.

    fantasy mutiny larceny prank

Using Words Wisely: No. 2

In each sentence, one word has been omitted. Read each sentence and the words that follow. Circle the word that completes the sentence in the **most meaningful way.**

1. Because he couldn't complete his task, Dan became ____________ and frustrated.
   ill cheerful discouraged evil

2. Many animals, when threatened, become very ____________.
   attractive maligned acceptive aggressive

3. Andrew, who loves dinosaurs, would like to become a ____________.
   geologist zoologist astronaut paleontologist

4. Our factory will ____________ your product easily.
   manufacture fracture caricature embark

5. To solve their building needs creatively, the ____________ will be very important.
   architect archaeologist mason engineer

6. John, who is ____________, usually pronounces words correctly.
   situate punctuate articulate unctuous

7. Sally became ____________ at the sight of the mouse.
   pedigreed pedagogic petrified petroleum

8. The wind made a ____________ noise through the tree leaves.
   breaking munching whistling banging

9. Brian's favorite event at swim meets is the ____________.
   leap crawl flip goal

10. When Kristi won the cooking contest, she felt ____________.
    anxious excited discouraged wrecked

11. Pat had trouble getting all eight sides of the ____________ even.
    hexagon paragon octagon pentagon

12. Dad helped the boys build a ____________ for their rabbits.
    cabin stable hutch deck

Using Words Wisely: No. 2, Cont.

13. The pebble in Frank's shoe was very ____________.

    helpful   sore   irritating   woeful

14. Because Marie dislikes clutter, she ____________ old, unused things.

    saves   remembers   helps   discards

15. Rob used the trunk to ____________ his gear.

    repair   stow   disinfect   dangerous

16. The ____________ of the barn is where Kari's family stores the hay.

    ceiling   loft   patio   column

17. Beth places too much ____________ on trivial matters.

    problems   importance   serious   respect

18. The room was ____________clean.

    electricity   immaculately   solidify   neutralized

19. Shakespeare was a great ____________.

    landmark   waterfall   wheelwright   playwright

20. The announcer has a clear, ____________ voice.

    harsh   fragile   pleasant   soft

21. The downpour ____________ the garden.

    drenched   delineated   reported   composed

22. The box of ____________ was labeled "FRAGILE."

    pans   mallets   anvils   goblets

23. This ____________ is very thirst-quenching.

    percolator   resonator   amplifier   beverage

24. The storm is ____________ quickly.

    fossilizing   actively   approaching   fracturing

Using Words Wisely: No. 3

In each sentence, one word has been omitted. Read each sentence and the words that follow. Circle the word that completes the sentence in the **most meaningful way.**

1. The ____________ took the passengers and their cars across the river.
   sailboat yacht tugboat ferry

2. Sir Lancelot wore a coat of ____________.
   wool leather armor fur

3. Anne went to the ____________ to get medicine for her mother.
   nursery library pharmacy haberdashery

4. The ____________ took care of the cat's broken leg.
   zoologist dentist optometrist veterinarian

5. A dog is sometimes called a ____________.
   canine reptile feline simian

6. Carol ____________ her canoe toward the beach.
   drove moved ran paddled

7. Farmers ____________ their land before they plant.
   examine harvest cultivate water

8. By experimenting, scientists ____________ answers to many problems.
   seek copy prevent use

9. Because the waiting line was long, people got ____________.
   lonely tired quiet nervous

10. Fictional books contain ____________ tales.
    real biographical imaginary delightful

11. The autumn leaves ____________ to the ground.
    stumbled drifted flowed jumped

12. Labor and management needed a(n) ____________ party to settle the dispute.
    argumentative prejudiced impartial biased

Using Words Wisely: No. 3, Cont.

13. They tried to ____________ the annoying sound of the loud music.
    raise   suppress   publish   promote

14. You must ____________ your key into the lock in order to open the door.
    fasten   join   insert   latch

15. Long wooden spears called ____________ were carried by knights.
    mallets   laths   maces   lances

16. Carlos went for a ride in a ____________, an airplane with one set of wings.
    monoplane   biplane   helicopter   blimp

17. Elaine, always the ____________, believed that everything would turn out for the best.
    pessimist   optometrist   pragmatist   optimist

18. Many southern colonists lived on large cotton ____________.
    farms   plantations   fields   settlements

19. The delighted children listened to the storyteller with ____________ attention.
    limited   scant   diverse   rapt

20. The rooms in the mansion were ____________ enough to hold all of the furniture.
    spacious   decorated   pleasant   expensive

21. Because of her experience, she was fully ____________ to do the job.
    available   unsuitable   qualified   willing

22. If it hadn't rained, the outdoor party would have been ____________.
    over   ruined   set   successful

23. Although it cost only a small amount, the suit looked ____________.
    expensive   cheap   common   old

24. The ____________ television show almost put me to sleep.
    exciting   boring   short   funny

Using Words Wisely: No. 4

In each sentence, one word has been omitted. Read each sentence and the words that follow. Circle the word that completes the sentence in the **most meaningful way.**

1. The doctor used the ____________ to clean a wound.
   stethoscope hemostat snaffle syringe

2. Because he played the trumpet, he sat in the ____________ section.
   brass woodwind percussion string

3. His ____________ hangs above the mantel.
   ascot portrait landmark alias

4. The main points of the study were included in a ____________ report.
   literary resume contract summary

5. After he injured his leg, David ____________ home.
   walked hobbled jogged ran

6. I ____________ a check in the letter that I sent to you.
   enclosed kept found received

7. The writer liked the out-of-the-way cabin because it was so ____________.
   busy secluded sedate seditious

8. The placid fisherman showed great ____________ while waiting for a catch.
   weariness anger annoyance patience

9. Since they have become ____________, tomatoes are sold at a lower cost.
   scarce abundant choice uncommon

10. Mr. Grant hired a lawyer to ____________ his case.
    consider judge practice plead

11. Emily, a considerate person, is always ____________ to older people.
    respectful respective respectable respecting

12. Since Doug has cut down on calories, he has noticed a(n) ____________ in his weight.
    reduction increase upsurge expansion

Using Words Wisely: No. 4, Cont.

13. Because she was a weak person, her friends ____________ her.

    liked   dominated   avoided   scared

14. A long-distance runner should have a great deal of ____________.

    time   money   space   energy

15. The novelist added a(n) ____________ to her autobiography.

    anecdote   anarchist   antidote   portrait

16. Latin is difficult, but I think I can meet the ____________.

    course   homework   language   challenge

17. The bright yellow room is always sunny and ____________.

    cheerful   restful   joyless   crowded

18. The ____________ of covered wagons traveled together for safety reasons.

    flock   bunch   caravan   cluster

19. Hidden rocks can be a ____________ to boats.

    signal   mooring   buoy   hazard

20. The ____________ completed a study of the earth's physical features.

    geologist   agriculturist   botanist   architect

21. The ballroom has a seating ____________ of two hundred people.

    arrangement   capacity   order   system

22. Her ____________ was pleased with the quality of her work.

    friend   neighbor   employer   mother

23. Lewis and Clark displayed ____________ during their exploration of new lands.

    direction   courage   dread   power

24. In the sport of ____________, a target is important.

    soccer   baseball   archery   tennis

Using Words Wisely: No. 5

In each sentence, one word has been omitted. Read each sentence and the words that follow. Circle the word that completes the sentence in the **most meaningful way.**

1. The fireplace kept the room warm and ____________.
   moist cozy tender bare

2. ____________ is small bits of paper, twigs, and other materials used to start a fire.
   Soot Flax Coal Tinder

3. You will learn about ____________ when you study paleontology.
   resins fossils paintings operas

4. Bill's collection of maps is almost like having a(n) ____________.
   dictionary hemisphere atlas encyclopedia

5. Earthworms and snails are both ____________.
   reptiles invertebrates insects grids

6. The marble ____________ support the gigantic roof.
   floors tiles columns domes

7. The best tool found by Joe for moving snow was a ____________.
   hoe spade rake shears

8. Japan, China and Thailand are part of the ____________.
   karate Arctic Orient West

9. When green plants make their own food, it is called ____________.
   microprotein photosynthesis lipolysis calorimetry

10. People who want to lose weight should reduce the ____________ in their meals.
    vegetables minerals calories liquids

11. ____________ Mark is not a musician, he enjoys concerts.
    About Around Although Because

12. He knows many languages, so Tom has been asked to be a(n) ____________.
    median interloper interpreter dilettante

Using Words Wisely: No. 5, Cont.

13. Mary's understanding of logic usually helps her in ____________.

    housework weeding math laundry

14. Because Sally didn't have much time to read the story, she got the ____________ copy of the book.

    evaporated condensed lengthened shorthand

15. Jason likes to use his ____________ to separate sunlight into colors.

    viola ermine prism mahogany

16. Nicole, a successful dancer, has ____________ legs.

    weak strong auburn polite

17. Tara ____________ the play more than the others.

    vitalized mesmerized cataloged appreciated

18. This new microscope has ____________ magnification.

    anxious powerful active enforceable

19. Because of her busy schedule, Linda ____________ her lunch time.

    remembered lengthened abbreviated dictated

20. His ____________ helps Johnny be very creative.

    memorization imagination punctuation allergies

21. What ____________ have you made for your trip?

    preparations answers comparisons focus

22. The constant interruptions were very ____________.

    relaxing comforting annoying cleansing

23. Solving word problems requires ____________ reading.

    careless unusual heedless careful

24. Her new car was a ____________ of enjoyment.

    epilogue source apology pedestal

Using Words Wisely: No. 6

In each sentence, one word has been omitted. Read each sentence and the words that follow. Circle the word that completes the sentence in the **most meaningful way.**

1. Johnny's main ____________ is model building.
   illness hobby exit container

2. The polar bear is one of the few ____________ of the arctic area.
   villains malingers inhabitants terms

3. Snakes and ____________ are members of the reptile family.
   mice lizards oxen wasps

4. Marshes and riverbanks are good places for ____________ cattails.
   meeting locating freezing racing

5. Gods and goddesses are ____________ in ancient myths.
   punctuated fared reasoned characters

6. Cheryl used the ____________ to help prepare the batter.
   griddle mixer sieve colander

7. Medical school was difficult, but Joe ____________ it would be worth it.
   convinced stressed wished realized

8. Raising children is very ____________.
   thoughtful rewarding careful favored

9. Metamorphosis is ____________ to butterflies and frogs.
   unusual natural near famous

10. Dolores, a(n) ____________ person, doesn't hesitate to hug her friends.
    honest serious nervous affectionate

11. A(n) ____________ meal is one that has many healthy ingredients.
    anxious fractious nutritious negative

12. The ____________ of a hurricane is usually calm.
    tooth eye head mouth

Using Words Wisely: No. 6, Cont.

13. The dentist checked my ____________ yesterday.
    incus   molar   tibia   femur

14. I like classical music in ____________ to popular music.
    accordance   addition   extinction   perception

15. He behaved ____________ in a dangerous situation.
    gleefully   bravely   lively   lowly

16. The gale ____________ winds were the strongest!
    stormed   turned   easy   force

17. The paper clip held the papers ____________.
    securely   attractively   randomly   ruggedly

18. She attached the spinnaker to the ____________.
    spinning wheel   spinet   sedan   sailboat

19. Because the refrigerator was not ____________, the food spoiled.
    distressing   navigation   functioning   recording

20. It was difficult to watch television because of the ____________.
    inflation   static   irradiator   phosphates

21. The birthday ____________ was enjoyed by everyone.
    employ   regeneration   celebration   perception

22. The fracture was ____________ by the x-ray.
    convinced   extinct   identified   healed

23. Use the sponge to ____________ that spill.
    enlarge   erase   blot   habitat

24. An earthquake can be a(n) ____________ force of nature.
    infrared   inflated   timorous   devastating

SECTION III
Determine the Meaning

Suggested Time: 15 minutes
(1 minutes for directions)
(14 minutes for competitive activity)

This section contains vocabulary activity pages. Students are required to use context clues and inferential thinking to determine the meaning of identified words. The correct answer is the word that comes closest in meaning to the selected word.

Directions for Use as Self-Directed Activities:
Distribute the materials to the students, who will complete the work independently. As self-directed activities, the sheets are especially useful as warm-up activities, supplementary lessons, homework assignments, and independent extensions.

Directions for Use as Competitive Activities:
Divide the students into teams. Allow one minute to explain the directions and scoring and fourteen minutes for students to complete the activities. The time allotted will vary with the ability level of the class. When the allotted time has expired, or when all the students have completed the sheets, total the number of correct responses. Award one point for each correct answer. Tally each team member's points and record the group's total points on the scoresheet. For example, 14 correct responses = 14 points. If the activity is done as a team effort with members calling out the answers and a member writing them on the chalkboard, the scoring is also one point for each correct answer.

Determine the Meaning: No. 1

Read each sentence carefully. Circle the word below the sentence that comes closest in meaning to the word in bold.

1. They arranged a **conference**.
   meeting interview debate agreement

2. Silver is a **precious** metal.
   rare cheap common valuable

3. A **vast** mountain range was seen in the distance.
   beautiful huge grassy rocky

4. They lived in a **rural** area.
   city desirable country urban

5. The desk was **strewn** with papers.
   decorated piled adorned covered

6. The child's cries **ceased**.
   increased lessened ended started

7. The **decoy** was used by the hunter.
   gun trap animal lure

8. The curator showed us a **bogus** painting.
   unusual expensive fake creative

9. The room was decorated in a **garish** manner.
   attractive tasteful flashy unique

10. He wore a **disguise**.
    suit camouflage cloak coat

11. Mr. Gray's position was **elevated**.
    raised praised essential lowered

12. The postman handled a **fragile** package.
    heavy sturdy breakable light

13. The sick child was **isolated**.
    feverish unhappy hospitalized secluded

14. The meeting ended in **harmony**.
    accord melody commitment conflict

Determine the Meaning: No. 2

Read each sentence carefully. Circle the word below the sentence that comes closest in meaning to the word in bold.

1. Mr. Jones is a busy **merchant**.
   scientist businessman explorer writer

2. Patty is an **energetic** girl.
   pretty pleasant active clever

3. Uncle Charlie is **eccentric** at times.
   artistic strange cranky grouchy

4. This painting **depicts** a sunset.
   forms hides conceals shows

5. The cabin was a **crude** home.
   rough fancy small open

6. **Hark**, do you hear that bird?
   stop run listen quiet

7. That dress is a **peculiar** shade of purple.
   odd excellent beautiful ordinary

8. Have you seen the **display** at the office?
   equipment exhibit furniture paperwork

9. Where does the stream **meander**?
   begin flow wander end

10. It was an **artificial** fur jacket.
    natural insulated expensive synthetic

11. Her feelings are very **genuine**.
    real abnormal phony comical

12. The Statue of Liberty is **colossal**.
    patriotic gigantic symbolic electrified

13. Can you repair the **puncture** in my tires?
    slash tear hole liner

14. Congress can **impeach** the President.
    elect accuse pardon veto

Determine the Meaning: No. 3

Read each sentence carefully. Circle the word below the sentence that comes closest in meaning to the word in bold.

1. **Coax** him to play the game.
   ask persuade trick force

2. There was a **commotion** in the classroom.
   disturbance visitor surprise lesson

3. Put a **muzzle** on the animal.
   leash license mouth covering chain

4. It was a **solemn** occasion.
   happy noisy serious busy

5. They sat under the **boughs** of the trees.
   leaves flowers shade limbs

6. The lot was **vacant.**
   empty dirty crowded weeded

7. The woman was **thrifty** with her money.
   foolish generous frugal thoughtful

8. The **pharmacist** worked late.
   doctor dentist druggist lawyer

9. He had a **prediction** about the weather.
   discussion question prophecy comment

10. The water was **scalding** my hand.
    cold warm burning tepid

11. The **facade** of the building looked attractive.
    front rear interior porch

12. The boy was **hostile** to his sister.
    friendly helpful antagonistic kind

13. I saw that he was my **foe**.
    companion friend enemy follower

14. I made an **accurate** measurement.
    long wrong crooked true

Determine the Meaning: No. 4

Read each sentence carefully. Circle the word below the sentence that comes closest in meaning to the word in bold.

1. Janet was **confident** that she could do the job.
   doubtful positive nervous modest

2. A **cautious** person thinks before acting.
   happy assured helpful wary

3. We were grateful for the **generous** gift.
   lavish unique needed inexpensive

4. Her **greedy** uncle kept the money.
   rude miserly poor mean

5. The **impatient** child started to cry.
   small sick injured restless

6. Try to be **considerate** of other people.
   cautious thoughtful cooperative critical

7. There was a great deal of **humidity** in the air.
   moisture pollution sunshine fogginess

8. The large factory was now **idle**.
   ideal inactive thriving expanding

9. The **occupant** of the house was missing.
   doorbell address gate resident

10. Jim kept up the family **traditions**.
    beliefs jobs standards customs

11. The carpenters **partitioned** the room.
    divided painted papered fixed

12. The hard work was **necessary**.
    difficult needed reasonable expected

13. The weather looked **dismal**.
    dreary cheerful cold promising

14. Her dancing seemed **effortless**.
    complex clumsy tiring easy

Determine the Meaning: No. 5

Read each sentence carefully. Circle the word or phrase below the sentence that comes closest in meaning to the word in bold.

1. Tony understood the **concept** well.
   idea   average   beginning   choice

2. Jane could not **grasp** the branch.
   conquer   understand   know   grab

3. In chess, you'd like to **seize** the queen.
   subtract   capture   overthrow   borrow

4. Each piece of furniture in the palace had its own **sheen**.
   value   glow   place   color

5. Always **examine** all the possibilities.
   grade   investigate   list   remember

6. The flower was very **dainty**.
   delicate   large   heavy   expensive

7. Our **intent** was to get to class on time.
   action   call   aim   benefit

8. What **form** will you give your project?
   structure   cover   advertisement   drawings

9. You must write **a minimum of** three paragraphs.
   at least   at most   more than   less than

10. We searched **frantically** for the lost puppy.
    calmly   all over   excitedly   somewhat

11. Pat dressed carefully for the **frigid** day.
    humid   wonderful   freezing   somewhat

12. Meg wore a **pinafore** over her dress.
    apron   coat   jacket   cape

13. We thought it was a **bizarre** story.
    mystery   weird   adventure   comic

14. Let the lizard continue to **bask** in the sun.
    grow quickly   eat a lot   warm itself   fight

Determine the Meaning: No. 6

Read each sentence carefully. Circle the word below the sentence that comes closest in meaning to the word in bold.

1. I'm **positive** that we will win the game.
   hopeful sure afraid doubtful

2. Can you **imitate** my handwriting?
   copy guess change locate

3. Bill was a **reckless** driver.
   good fast careless calm

4. Don't listen to **gossip**.
   music news strangers rumors

5. His boss gave him a **bonus**.
   reward job desk office

6. I noticed a broken **fender** on my car.
   tail light wheel guard brake bumper

7. Their trip was filled with **hazards**.
   fun souvenirs dangers tours

8. His speech was **humorous**.
   amusing long boring interesting

9. Did they **contribute** their help?
   hold give offer allow

10. The team had one **defeat**.
    win tie victory loss

11. Do not **delay** the race.
    cancel start shorten postpone

12. The town is **distant**.
    far small near crowded

13. She acted in a **foolish** manner.
    silly proud excited clever

14. The dog was **loyal** to his master.
    nasty friendly angry faithful

Determine the Meaning: No. 7

Read each sentence carefully. Circle the word below the sentence that comes closest in meaning to the word in bold.

1. The time is **dwindling**; please hurry!
   growing shrinking increasing worrying

2. Our vacation will take us to **tropical** countries.
   many hot foreign cold

3. Getting married is a **momentous** decision.
   difficult nervous important energetic

4. "Are you **certain** of your answer?" asked Beth.
   remembering sure mindful unsteady

5. Whales and dolphins are **marine** mammals.
   swimming beautiful ocean air

6. Bill was **anxious** about taking the test.
   forgetful happy sure nervous

7. Set your **goals** high.
   aims ideas sounds trees

8. **Imagine** you are living on the moon.
   remember pretend realize impress

9. Her project is **incomplete**.
   educational pretty unfinished wrecked

10. Doing that is **illegal**.
    lawful necessary important unlawful

11. Kelly chose an **unusual** color as her favorite.
    average popular strange normal

12. The mouse **concealed** itself in the burrow.
    ran hid waited fed

13. "Do not **magnify** the problem," said their mother.
    forget repeat enlarge make

14. The **crafty** fox escaped the hunters.
    brave shrewd silly pretty

Determine the Meaning: No. 8

Read each sentence carefully. Circle the word below the sentence that comes closest in meaning to the word in bold.

1. Mark gave the rope a quick **jerk**.
   pat mix rub pull

2. The woman in the painting wore a **kerchief**.
   cape hat hood scarf

3. The monster **lurked** in the shadows.
   sneaked played slept paraded

4. "Don't **lunge** at me like that," said Tom.
   throw laugh reach look

5. I will **instruct** you how to do this.
   remind teach build list

6. Michelle works on her **journal** every day.
   appliance diary painting puzzle

7. What **process** did you use to finish this so quickly?
   name drawing tools method

8. There are **ample** parking spaces in the lot.
   many few none some

9. We got the information at the **tourist** center.
   passenger airport art visitor

10. The **immature** apple was picked too early.
    soft sour unripened golden

11. We went **surf** fishing last week.
    river bay lake ocean

12. Our ancestors are **deceased**.
    dead beautiful angry cautious

13. Please lower the **volume** of that music.
    amount range loudness mixture

14. Pam was not **aware** of the coming storm.
    ignorant afraid knowledgeable thinking

Determine the Meaning: No. 9

Read each sentence carefully. Circle the word below the sentence that comes closest in meaning to the word in bold.

1. Bill was **envious** of his brother's new car.
   notified jealous annoyed accepting
2. They decided to purchase a **flawless** gem.
   genuine shiny perfect delicate
3. The air was **stagnant** because the breeze had stopped.
   stale moist cool delightful
4. Colorful and **exotic** flowers grew on the island.
   fragrant strange beautiful large
5. The long ride home seemed **monotonous** to the restless children.
   exciting pleasant special boring
6. Lisa was **apprehensive** about her math scores.
   happy confident worried angry
7. The skies looked dark and **ominous**.
   cloudy rainy threatening starry
8. The journey across the mountain was **perilous**.
   long dangerous tiring slow
9. Chopping the logs into firewood is an **arduous** task.
   easy annoying difficult necessary
10. Economic growth was **sluggish** around the world.
    rapid flourishing strong slow
11. The patriotic music was **inspiring**.
    loud stirring soft rhythmic
12. Steve was **famished** because he missed his dinner.
    upset happy sick starved
13. He tried to **restrain** the vicious dog.
    confine release replace hide
14. The frightened child started to **quiver**.
    cry shake run scream

Determine the Meaning: No. 10

Read each sentence carefully. Circle the word below the sentence that comes closest in meaning to the word in bold.

1. At the sight of the snake we were **petrified**.
   excited annoyed frightened angry

2. That butterfly was a **rare** sight.
   unusual beautiful common ugly

3. You are in **peril** standing on the broken ladder.
   water friendship danger closer

4. The **contented** baby slept well.
   chubby ill peaceful playful

5. We were told to **cease** the loud music.
   stop continue increase enjoy

6. Mark has injured his **shin**.
   spine ear leg foot

7. Please move to the rear **promptly**.
   orderly nicely easily quickly

8. Mike wants to become a **physician**.
   scientist builder artist doctor

9. It was an **anonymous** phone call.
   identified unknown funny helpful

10. Nicole is a **reliable** girl.
    sensitive dependable cute creative

11. A hawk is a **predator** of mice and rabbits.
    bird hunter rival friend

12. The traffic was **congested** near the park entrance.
    thin fast accented clogged

13. **Occasionally** I like to try something different.
    frequently sometimes often never

14. Jack will **decipher** the secret message.
    send read decode receive

Determine the Meaning: No. 11

Read each sentence carefully. Circle the word below the sentence that comes closest in meaning to the word in bold.

1. The water in the lake was **transparent**.
   clear cold rippled deep
2. The young man was big and **brawny**.
   fat muscular bossy athletic
3. Sally **cherished** her first-prize trophy.
   accepted won held treasured
4. The **identical** twins shared a bedroom.
   different separate alike friendly
5. It is your **obligation** to complete the job.
   duty pleasure wish hope
6. My **opponent** won the game.
   friend rival classmate teammate
7. The structure was built to be **permanent**.
   used elegant lasting grand
8. We met the **previous** owners of the house.
   former new prospective prosperous
9. There was a **scanty** supply of food left.
   large abundant meager delicious
10. The sudden storm made the group **scatter**.
    separate angry sad wet
11. The boy seemed **sullen** after the argument.
    confident sensitive apologetic gloomy
12. The joke he told was **absurd**.
    ridiculous nasty boring logical
13. The lighthouse keeper enjoyed his **solitude**.
    job environment seclusion view
14. The angry soldiers planned a **rebellion**.
    demonstration petition trick uprising

SECTION IV
Sequencing

Suggested Time: 15 minutes
(1 minutes for directions)
(14 minutes for competitive activity)

In this section students are asked to put words in a proper sequence in order to form a logical paragraph. (Answers may differ from those given. If the sequence makes sense, award credit for it.)

EXAMPLE:

3 The Constitution was signed on September 17, 1787.
1 The United States was governed by the Articles of Confederation.
4 The Bill of Rights was added to protect our individual rights.
5 The 26th amendment gave 18-year-olds the right to vote.
2 George Washington was chosen as president of the Constitutional Convention.

Directions for Use as Self-Directed Activities:
Distribute the materials to the students, who will complete the work independently. As self-directed activities, the sheets are especially useful as warm-up activities, supplementary lessons, homework assignments, and independent extensions.

Directions for Use as Competitive Activities:
Divide the students into teams. Allow one minute to explain the directions and scoring and fourteen minutes for students to complete the activities. The time allotted will vary with the ability level of the class. When the allotted time has expired, or when all the students have completed the sheets, total the number of correct responses. Award one point for each entirely correct set of sentences. Tally each team member's points and record the group's total points on the scoresheet. For example, 3 entirely correct responses = 3 points. If the activity is done as a team effort with members calling out the answers and a member writing them on the chalkboard, the scoring is also one point for each totally correct set of sentences.

Sequencing: No. 1

The sentences in these paragraphs are out of order. Place the numerals 1 to 5 next to each sentence to form the proper sequence.

1: **ABRAHAM LINCOLN**

____ He was President during the Civil War.

____ He was assassinated in Ford's Theatre, Washington, D.C.

____ Abraham Lincoln was the sixteenth President of the U.S.

____ He participated in a series of pre-election debates with Stephen Douglas.

____ His "Gettysburg Address" is a world famous speech.

2: **DIAMONDS**

____ The carat is the unit of measurement for these brilliant stones.

____ They are a terrifically hard substance formed of a carbon compound.

____ Diamonds are highly valued gemstones.

____ South Africa produces most of the world's supply of diamonds.

____ They also reflect light brilliantly.

3: **SOCCER**

____ Each team tries to propel the ball into the other's goal.

____ Players may not use their hands or arms to move the ball forward or to score a goal.

____ Soccer, known as football in most countries, is an exciting team sport.

____ The "goalies," however, may use their hands when they are within a specific area.

____ There are two teams, each with eleven players.

4: **THE SMITHSONIAN INSTITUTE**

____ Although he never visited the U.S., he made a gift of $550,000 to start it.

____ The building was completed in 1852.

____ There is no admission fee, and it is a marvelous place to visit.

____ It was begun by James Smithson, an Englishman.

____ The Smithsonian Institute, dedicated to learning, is in Washington, D.C.

Sequencing: No. 2

The sentences in these paragraphs are out of order. Place the numerals 1 to 5 next to each sentence to form the proper sequence.

1: **A CHILLY DAY**

____ Although the heater was on, Anne felt chilly.

____ Finally, she sat nearer to the fireplace.

____ She made herself some hot cocoa.

____ Anne was still cold, so she put on a sweater, too.

____ The day was the coldest on record.

2: **A CELEBRATION CAKE**

____ The decorations were carefully done.

____ After the cake cooled, Mom iced it with Andrew's favorite frosting.

____ The eggs were added to the batter one at a time.

____ Mother decided a special dessert was in order.

____ Everyone enjoyed a large serving.

3: **A SNOWY DAY**

____ Gradually, the snow came down harder and harder.

____ The children built a snow fort and went sledding.

____ When the snowstorm was finally over, 7 inches had fallen.

____ The first flakes were large and fluffy.

____ You could barely see across the yard.

4: **STAINED GLASS**

____ A full-size drawing, called a cartoon, is made.

____ Stained glass is colored glass used in decorative windows in religious and public buildings.

____ The cartoon is used as a blueprint; each section is numbered.

____ The pieces of glass are held by lead cams.

____ Finally, details are then painted on where needed.

Sequencing: No. 3

The sentences in these paragraphs are out of order. Place the numerals 1 to 5 next to each sentence to form the proper sequence.

1: **MOON STUDY**

____ In 1969 it became the first object in space visited by humans.

____ In 335 B.C. Aristotle used lunar eclipses to prove the earth was ball-shaped.

____ In ancient times the moon, Earth's closest neighbor, may have been only 10,000 miles away.

____ George H. Darwin, in 1879, suggested that the moon and Earth were once one body.

____ In 1972 another group of U.S. astronauts visited the moon.

2: **THE TELEPHONE**

____ Many improvements have since developed.

____ It is now possible to use a telephone in almost any nation of the world.

____ Alexander Graham Bell invented the telephone in 1876.

____ Telephone operators connected almost all calls manually through a switchboard until the 1900s.

____ A few years later—in 1880—the American Bell Telephone Company was formed.

3: **TERRARIUMS**

____ Place the cover on the container.

____ Carefully place the plants in the moist soil and clean the container's sides.

____ A terrarium is a small garden enclosed in a transparent container.

____ Prepare one by layering small pebbles, broken charcoal, and potting soil.

____ Moisten well, but do not make it muddy.

4: **COLUMBUS**

____ Christopher Columbus was born in Italy in 1451.

____ He thought he could reach the Indies by sailing west across the ocean.

____ As a young man he worked with his brother as a mapmaker.

____ In 1492 he discovered the lands now called America.

____ King Ferdinand and Queen Isabella of Spain agreed to pay for the journey.

Sequencing: No. 4

The sentences in these paragraphs are out of order. Place the numerals 1 to 5 next to each sentence to form the proper sequence.

1: **SKELETAL SYSTEM**

____ The largest of the 206 bones are in our legs, and the smallest bones are in the ears.

____ As the body grows, many of the bones fuse, or grow together.

____ When a person with a normal skeletal system reaches adulthood, he has 206 bones.

____ A baby has about 305 bones.

____ The bones in a human body make up the skeletal system.

2: **GEORGE WASHINGTON CARVER**

____ More than 300 products were developed from the peanut alone.

____ George Washington Carver is renowned for his contributions to agriculture.

____ During his lifetime, Carver received many honors for his work.

____ He created new products from peanuts, sweet potatoes, and pecans.

____ In 1945, two years after his death, Congress declared January 5th as George Washington Carver Day.

3: **THE PYRAMIDS**

____ Thousands of workers were needed to carry the huge stone blocks.

____ It took many years to build the pyramids.

____ The pyramids are famous structures.

____ After their construction was completed, the pyramids were used as tombs for Egyptian kings.

____ They are located near the Nile River.

4: **ARTHROPODS**

____ The hard covering is called an exoskeleton.

____ Three-fourths of all animals are classified as arthropods.

____ They can also be recognized by their hard shells.

____ All these animals are invertebrates with jointed legs.

____ Arthropods include insects, arachnids, and crustaceans.

Sequencing: No. 5

The sentences in these paragraphs are out of order. Place the numerals 1 to 5 next to each sentence to form the proper sequence.

1: **THOMAS EDISON**

____ Thomas Alva Edison was one of the world's greatest inventors.

____ He discovered a filament that would produce electricity.

____ Much of his noted work was completed at his New Jersey laboratories.

____ This led to the invention of the electric light bulb.

____ One problem that Edison solved in his laboratories was the production of electricity.

2: **WEATHER INFORMATION**

____ These satellites orbit the earth and take pictures of the earth's atmosphere.

____ Weather maps help meteorologists forecast the weather.

____ Since 1960, they have also received help from weather satellites.

____ The meteorologists are able to see the atmospheric conditions in many regions by reading the maps.

____ They can also record air pressure on the maps by drawing lines called isobars.

3: **DETROIT**

____ Paints and medicines are produced there too.

____ It ranks first in the manufacturing of autos.

____ Detroit is an industrial city.

____ Because of this auto production, it is called the Motor City.

____ Besides autos, Detroit's products include brass and bronze tools and chemicals.

4: **BEAVERS' HOMES**

____ Each beaver family has its own home when completed.

____ In the ponds, they make lodges of sticks and mud.

____ Beavers build their homes in streams and lakes.

____ First, they create dams to form ponds.

____ The beavers enlarge and repair their lodges as long as they live in them.

Sequencing: No. 6

The sentences in these paragraphs are out of order. Place the numerals 1 to 5 next to each sentence to form the proper sequence.

1: **MEXICO**

____ Near the coasts, you will find low plains and jungle areas.

____ Mexico is a nation of geographical contrasts.

____ Most of the plateau area receives little rainfall and is quite arid.

____ Huge rugged mountain ranges rise from the plains.

____ Between the mountain ranges is a high plateau.

2: **SUGAR CANE**

____ Sugar cane is an important industry in Hawaii.

____ It takes about two years for the cane to ripen.

____ It is Hawaii's chief money crop.

____ Modern machinery is used to harvest the ripe sugar cane.

____ Sugar cane is usually grown in irrigated fields.

3: **HUSKING BEES**

____ Neighbors often got together for husking bees.

____ Two teams would compete to husk a pile of corn.

____ Pioneers were helpful to each other.

____ After the contest, the neighbors would enjoy a supper and a square dance.

____ During the bee, the outer leaves were removed from the ears of corn.

4: **OFFSHORE DRILLING**

____ Drilling platforms are towed out to sea so that the oil can be reached.

____ The legs of the platform are then secured on the bottom of the sea.

____ Petroleum is sometimes located beneath the water off the shore.

____ Once adjusted, these platforms can support all the drilling equipment.

____ Oil is then pumped through pipes into tankers.

SECTION V
Fact or Opinion

Suggested Time: 15 minutes
(1 minutes for directions)
(14 minutes for competitive activity)

In this section students are required to differentiate between fact and opinion statements. A **fact** is information that can be proved. An **opinion** is what a person thinks about something.

Directions for Use as Self-Directed Activities:
Distribute the materials to the students, who will complete the work independently. As self-directed activities, the sheets are especially useful as warm-up activities, supplementary lessons, homework assignments, and independent extensions.

Directions for Use as Competitive Activities:
Divide the students into teams. Allow one minute to explain the directions and scoring and fourteen minutes for students to complete the activities. The time allotted will vary with the ability level of the class. When the allotted time has expired, or when all the students have completed the sheets, total the number of correct responses. Award one point for each correct answer. Tally each team member's points and record the group's total points on the scoresheet. For example, 14 correct responses = 14 points. If the activity is done as a team effort with members calling out the answers and a member writing them on the chalkboard, the scoring is also one point for each correct answer.

Fact or Opinion: No. 1

Thunderstorms and Tornadoes

Circle F (fact) or O (opinion)

1. Thunderstorms are much more frequent in summer than in winter. **F** **O**
2. Thunderstorms are very frightening. **F** **O**
3. Tornadoes are more destructive than thunderstorms. **F** **O**
4. The path of a tornado is very narrow. **F** **O**
5. It is dangerous to stand under a tree during a lightning storm. **F** **O**
6. Lightning in the sky can be a beautiful sight. **F** **O**
7. Thunderstorms are common in the open prairie. **F** **O**
8. Tornadoes are often called twisters. **F** **O**
9. The best part of a thunderstorm is the rainbow that comes after it. **F** **O**
10. There is little that you can do to protect yourself from violent storms. **F** **O**
11. A tornado resembles a funnel-shaped cloud. **F** **O**
12. Hailstones from heavy rainfall can be as large as tennis balls. **F** **O**
13. Primitive people believed that thunder was the sound of angry gods. **F** **O**
14. A storm cellar is designed to provide protection from a tornado or cyclone. **F** **O**

Fact or Opinion: No. 2

Turtles

Circle F (fact) or O (opinion)

1.	A turtle is the only reptile that has a shell.	F	O
2.	Turtles make good pets for children.	F	O
3.	Turtles are cold-blooded animals.	F	O
4.	Governments should establish more turtle preserves.	F	O
5.	The Galapagos turtle is one of the largest land turtles.	F	O
6.	Some turtles live more than 100 years.	F	O
7.	Turtle meat is delicious.	F	O
8.	The pond marsh family of turtles is the most attractive.	F	O
9.	Snapping turtles can be dangerous.	F	O
10.	A turtle's shell acts as natural protection.	F	O
11.	Some humans kill turtles for their meat.	F	O
12.	Sea turtles are faster swimmers than mud turtles.	F	O
13.	Turtles are generally friendly animals.	F	O
14.	Some turtles can move faster than a human on level ground.	F	O

Fact or Opinion: No. 3

Airplanes

Circle F (fact) or O (opinion)

1. Airplanes are the safest means of travel. **F O**
2. In 1500, Leonardo da Vinci made drawings of flying machines. **F O**
3. You must be at least 17 years of age to obtain a pilot's license in the U.S. **F O**
4. Early plane designers showed unusual skills. **F O**
5. Flaps and ailerons control the airplane's wings. **F O**
6. Designers test new airplanes long before they are ready for production. **F O**
7. An airplane assembly plant is similar to an automobile assembly plant. **F O**
8. The take-off is the most exciting and difficult part of a flight. **F O**
9. "Stalling speed" is the lowest speed that a plane can move without losing altitude. **F O**
10. At first, people paid little attention to the Wright brothers' new invention. **F O**
11. Navigating without visible landmarks is called "dead reckoning." **F O**
12. Radar is used to detect distant objects. **F O**
13. The job of air traffic controller is just as important as pilot. **F O**
14. Charles Lindbergh was a more daring pilot than Amelia Earhart. **F O**

Fact or Opinion: No. 4

The Human Heart

Circle F (fact) or O (opinion)

1. Your heart is about the size of your fist. **F O**
2. The heart is the most important organ in the body. **F O**
3. Heart surgeons are more skilled than brain surgeons. **F O**
4. Healthy heart muscle is very strong. **F O**
5. Heart transplants have been successful for over twenty years. **F O**
6. Six quarts of blood are pumped each minute by a healthy heart. **F O**
7. The aorta is the most important blood vessel. **F O**
8. Veins are more necessary than arteries to the heart. **F O**
9. Blood pressure is an indicator of the health of the heart. **F O**
10. The pulse is the speed at which the heart beats. **F O**
11. Children have the healthiest hearts. **F O**
12. The stethoscope is the best tool a doctor has for examining the heart. **F O**
13. CPR is a training course to help people save the lives of others. **F O**
14. Regulators, called valves, control the flow of blood through the heart itself. **F O**

Fact or Opinion: No. 5

Electricity

Circle F (fact) or O (opinion)

1.	Electricity is the best source of energy.	F	O
2.	Electricity travels at the speed of light.	F	O
3.	Water is a good conductor of electricity.	F	O
4.	Benjamin Franklin discovered that lightning is a form of electricity.	F	O
5.	Telephones use a small amount of electricity.	F	O
6.	Static electricity is electricity at rest.	F	O
7.	Running water is a means of producing electricity.	F	O
8.	Thomas Edison's work with electricity was the most valuable scientific accomplishment of the twentieth century.	F	O
9.	Electricity can exert a mighty force.	F	O
10.	Electrons are the smallest particles of electricity.	F	O
11.	AA batteries are better than AAA batteries.	F	O
12.	Electricity and magnetism are closely related.	F	O
13.	Electricity is easy to create and control.	F	O
14.	Electricity is an important part of our lives.	F	O

Fact or Opinion: No. 6

Automobiles

Circle F (fact) or O (opinion)

1. The majority of U.S. autos are made in Detroit. **F O**
2. Robots weld some of the parts in factories. **F O**
3. Henry Ford was a pioneer automaker. **F O**
4. U.S. cars are better than foreign cars. **F O**
5. The Indianapolis 500 is the most important car race. **F O**
6. The Model A and the Model T were Fords. **F O**
7. There were steam engine cars before gasoline engines. **F O**
8. Horsepower is the measure of a car engine's power. **F O**
9. A sedan is more comfortable than a two-door car. **F O**
10. Some cars are capable of reaching speeds of more than 600 mph. **F O**
11. Computers help to control some car functions. **F O**
12. Automobiles are safer now than ever. **F O**
13. Some cars are powered by electricity, not by gasoline. **F O**
14. A "V-8" is a type of car engine. **F O**

SECTION VI
Interpreting

Suggested Time: 15 minutes
(1 minutes for directions)
(14 minutes for competitive activity)

In this section students are asked to analyze information that is provided in each selection. They will be challenged to use skills of deducting, inferring, literal comprehension, and summarizing.

Directions for Use as Self-Directed Activities:
Distribute the materials to the students, who will complete the work independently. As self-directed activities, the sheets are especially useful as warm-up activities, supplementary lessons, homework assignments, and independent extensions.

Directions for Use as Competitive Activities:
Divide the students into teams. Allow one minute to explain the directions and scoring and fourteen minutes for students to complete the activities. The time allotted will vary with the ability level of the class. When the allotted time has expired, or when all the students have completed the sheets, total the number of correct responses. Award one point for each correct answer. Tally each team member's points and record the group's total points on the scoresheet. For example, 14 correct responses = 14 points. If the activity is done as a team effort with members calling out the answers and a member writing them on the chalkboard, the scoring is also one point for each correct answer.

Interpreting: No. 1

Read the selection; then circle the letters which come before the correct answers.

Computers have become an essential part of our everyday lives. They are being used in a variety of ways to improve our lives. Computers can work very quickly to solve many kinds of problems. Airplanes can be programmed to take off, land, and be kept on course by computers. Robots that are used in industry are computer controlled to complete various tasks. Computers are used in schools to help students learn. Banks offer computer banking services that can cash checks or transfer money. Computers aid doctors in diagnosing illnesses and help to monitor patients' progress in hospitals. In the future, all customer shopping needs may be satisfied by home computers.

1. The main idea of this story is...
   a. Computers are complex machines.
   b. Computers improve health care.
   c. Computers are being put to many uses.

2. Computers are important because...
   a. School children can use them easily.
   b. They can answer a variety of human needs.
   c. They can help us with our shopping and banking.

3. This story suggests that...
   a. Air travel has improved because of computers.
   b. Banking is safer because of computers.
   c. Computer robots will be widely used.

4. The best title for this story is...
   a. The Computer Revolution
   b. Computers and Health
   c. Computer Programs

Interpreting: No. 2

Read the selection; then circle the letters which come before the correct answers.

Submarines are undersea craft that are used for many purposes. Some submarines explore the sea beds to conduct scientific research or salvage hunting. Other submarines engage in repair work on pipelines or cables. Most submarines are utilized by a nation's navy. During wartime, they patrol the seas and attack the enemy with their missiles. Nuclear-powered subs can remain beneath the surface of the sea for a long duration of time and can move faster while submerged than on the surface.

1. The main idea of this story is...
   a. Nuclear-powered submarines remain submerged for a long time.
   b. Submarines are helpful in explorations.
   c. Submarines are employed in a variety of tasks.

2. Nuclear submarines are more versatile than other subs because...
   a. They can be used to repair pipelines.
   b. They can remain submerged for longer periods of time.
   c. They can launch missiles.

3. This story suggests that...
   a. Submarines are the largest part of the navy.
   b. Submarines are most active during wartime.
   c. Submarines are expensive.

4. The best title for this story is...
   a. Undersea Adventure
   b. The Story of Submarines
   c. Submarines and the Navy

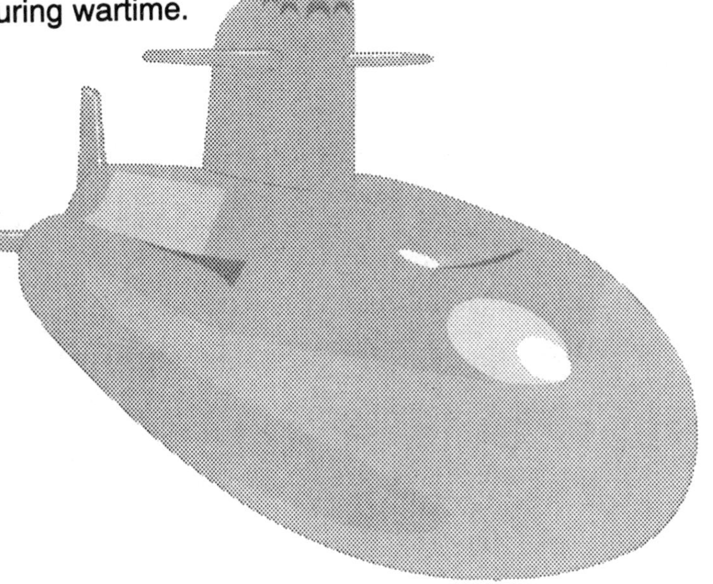

Interpreting: No. 3

Read the selection; then circle the letters which come before the correct answers.

Structures that help people shorten their journeys are called bridges. Although most are constructed to span bodies of water, some are built over land areas, and some are designed to connect buildings. Because their foundations need to be strong, most bridges are built from the bottom up. A beam bridge is the most popular type of bridge. Early bridges were made from wood; however, because these bridges could easily rot or catch on fire, they were replaced by steel. Suspension bridges can span long distances and are built high enough for boats to pass under them. These bridges are supported by cables. There are also many types of movable bridges that allow boats to sail safely through their channels.

1. The main idea of this story is…
   a. Suspension bridges are long.
   b. Bridges allow people to travel faster.
   c. Steel bridges are the strongest.

2. Boats can sail safely through suspension bridges because…
   a. They are very high.
   b. They are made of steel.
   c. They are movable.

3. This story suggests…
   a. Steel bridges last for a long time.
   b. Beam bridges are difficult to build.
   c. Movable bridges are the most popular.

4. The best title for this story would be…
   a. Early Bridges
   b. A World of Bridges
   c. Suspension Bridges

Interpreting: No. 4

Read the selection; then circle the letters which come before the correct answers.

Human skin is composed of millions of cells. The outer layer, called the epidermis, contains the dead cells; the underlayer, the dermis, is the living skin. Skin works to protect your body. The outer skin is very tough and is not damaged easily. Skin also helps to control your body temperature. When you sweat, your body cools. Your skin contains nerves that help you adjust to weather conditions, to pressure, and to pain. Sometimes skin is called the largest organ of the human body. It is always important to keep your skin clean so that the pores do not become infected.

1. The main idea of this story is...
   a. Millions of cells make up the human skin.
   b. The epidermis is the outer skin.
   c. Skin serves you in many ways.

2. Skin protects your body because...
   a. It guards against infection.
   b. It is the largest organ in the human body.
   c. It helps your body regulate heat.

3. This story suggests...
   a. The inner layer of skin is more important.
   b. The outer layer of skin is more fragile.
   c. Nerves in the skin transmit information.

4. The best title for this story would be...
   a. The Epidermis
   b. The Human Wrapper
   c. The Inner Skin

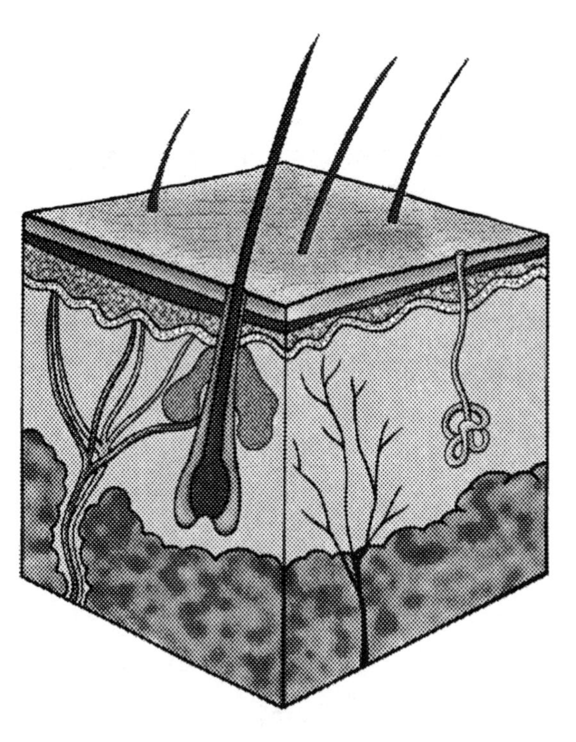

Interpreting: No. 5

Read the selection; then circle the letters which come before the correct answers.

Camels are well-adapted for life in the desert. They are able to exist for long periods of time without water. Their normal body temperature is 93°F during the night; however, during the day it may be as high as 104° to 105°F. Camels don't sweat the way humans do; they only lose water when their body temperature rises to 105°F. Camels store fat in their humps and turn it into food when they need it. The fleshy pads on their feet prevent them from sinking into the sand. Their long eyelashes protect them from flying dust. Camels have always been helpful to the nomads who wander the deserts of the world.

1. The main idea of the story is…

   a. Camels can be helpful creatures.

   b. Camels can live well in the desert.

   c. Camels have high body temperatures.

2. Camels are able to exist in deserts because…

   a. They are helpful to nomads.

   b. The can go for a long time without water.

   c. They can carry heavy loads.

3. This selection suggests that…

   a. Camels have a wider normal range of body temperature than humans.

   b. Camels have trouble walking in the sand.

   c. Camels like to carry heavy loads.

4. The best title for this story is…

   a. Creatures of the Desert

   b. Facts About Camels

   c. Desert Areas

Interpreting: No. 6

Read the selection; then circle the letters which come before the correct answers.

The first man-made satellite was launched in 1957 when the Soviet Union put *Sputnik* into orbit. The U.S. followed with *Explorer I,* launched in 1958. Today many man-made satellites orbit Earth and relay valuable information back to us. Weather satellites have television cameras that take pictures and warn us of approaching storms. There are communication satellites that alert us to news and events that occur all over the world. Navigation satellites help to guide ships at sea. Scientists use a variety of scientific satellites to learn more about the universe. Some of the satellites take photos of other planets and provide us with new facts about them.

1. The main idea of the story is...
   a. Communication satellites help us to keep in touch.
   b. Satellites are useful to mankind.
   c. The Soviet Union has more advanced satellites.

2. Scientific satellites are most useful because...
   a. They pass along messages.
   b. They are good fact-finders.
   c. They help sailors at sea.

3. This selection suggests that...
   a. Weather satellites help to save lives.
   b. We need to develop new types of satellites.
   c. The early satellites were small.

4. The best title for this story is...
   a. Outer Space
   b. Sputnik and Explorer
   c. Satellites Are Helpful

Interpreting: No. 7

Read the selection; then circle the letters which come before the correct answers.

Fertile areas in the middle of deserts are called oases. Water in these areas comes from under the ground or from mountain rivers. The largest oasis in the world is the Nile Valley. Oases are home to many plants and animals because of their abundant food and water supply. Graceful palm trees grow in some desert oases and insects, toads, and frogs use oases as breeding grounds. Farmers are able to grow crops in some desert oases. Large cities such as Cairo, Egypt, have developed in oasis areas.

1. The main idea of the story is...
   a. Large cities have developed in deserts.
   b. Crops need water to grow.
   c. People and animals are able to live in oases.

2. Oases are caused by...
   a. The presence of water.
   b. Animal and plant life.
   c. Development of cities.

3. This selection suggests that...
   a. Water is necessary to the continuation of life in deserts.
   b. Unusual plants and animals live in desert areas.
   c. Oases are uncommon places.

4. The best title for this story is...
   a. The Nile Valley
   b. Deserts Are Important
   c. Life In Oases

Interpreting: No. 8

Read the selection; then circle the letters which come before the correct answers.

In 1860, William H. Russell decided that he frontier needed a faster way to deliver mail. He hired young men to become Pony Express riders. Most riders were in their teens. The boys were required to weigh less than 130 pounds so that the horses would not be slowed down. The first delivery route went from Missouri to Sacramento, California. Often the riders found the overland route filled with danger and hazardous weather conditions. Indian wars were a constant concern. Bill Cody was a famous Pony Express rider. The new mail service was welcomed by the citizens of the area. Now it would take only ten days to receive mail!

1. The main idea of the story is…
   a. Only young boys could be riders.
   b. The Pony Express was a successful idea.
   c. The Pony Express was used in bad weather conditions.

2. This selection suggests that…
   a. Bill Cody was a hero.
   b. Thin boys could ride faster than heavier riders.
   c. The Pony Express service was not well received.

3. The selection suggests that William Russell started the Pony Express because…
   a. He wanted to open new western trails.
   b. He hoped to make a profit.
   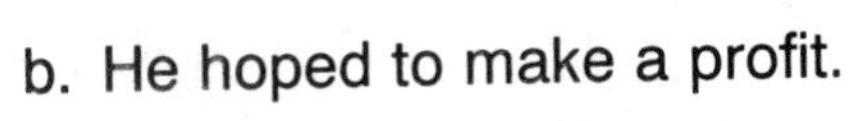
   c. Mail delivery in the west was slow.

4. The best title for this story is…
   a. The Overland Route
   b. The Wild Frontier
   c. A Speedy Mail Service

Interpreting: No. 9

Read the selection; then circle the letters which come before the correct answers.

The word "planet" means "wanderer." In order of their distance form the sun, the planets in our solar system are Mercury, Venus, Earth, Mars, Jupiter, Saturn, Uranus, Neptune, and Pluto. The closer to the sun, the warmer the planet. All of the planets revolve in orbits around the sun in the same direction. As they revolve around the sun, they also rotate. The planets are of various sizes and distances from the sun and from each other. Except for Earth, these heavenly bodies were named in honor of ancient Roman mythological characters.

1. The main idea of the story is…
   a. Earth was not named after a mythological character.
   b. There are nine planets in our solar system.
   c. Pluto is Mickey Mouse's dog.

2. This selection suggests that…
   a. Neptune travels in an orbit.
   b. Earth's orbit is larger than Jupiter's.
   c. Pluto's year is 1,900 "days."

3. This paragraph suggests that…
   a. Mars was the Roman god of war.
   b. Mars is not the same size as Earth.
   c. Mars is a warmer planet than Saturn.

4. The best title for this story is…
   a. Our Planetary System
   b. Space Travelers
   c. Martian Visitors

Interpreting: No. 10

Read the selection; then circle the letters which come before the correct answers.

The platypus lives near shallow streams and rivers in Australia and Tasmania. Although it is a true mammal, it lays eggs and has a snout like a duck's bill. What a strange animal! Making use of its webbed feet and broad, flat tail, the platypus is an excellent swimmer and diver. Its soft, thick fur once made it a favorite target of hunters. It uses its duckbill as a shovel to find mollusks, worms, and other life at the bottom of the water. Including its six-inch tail, the platypus may grow up to two feet in length.

1. This selection tells us...
   a. Platypuses were hunted nearly to extinction.
   b. Australian law forbids hunting platypuses now.
   c. The platypus does not live in the U.S.A.

2. This selection suggests that...
   a. The platypus is the strangest animal on Earth.
   b. Platypuses are not very large animals.
   c. The platypus is a great hunter.

3. This paragraph suggests that...
   a. The feet of the platypus are equipped with sharp claws.
   b. The shells of platypus eggs are soft and leathery.
   c. Platypuses may eat snails as part of their diet.

4. The best title for this story is...
   a. Wonders of Australia
   b. A Strange Mammal
   c. Webbed Feet

Interpreting: No. 11

Read the selection; then circle the letters which come before the correct answers.

Dinosaurs were reptiles that lived millions and millions of years ago. Like other reptiles, they laid eggs and were covered with scales. The word "dinosaur" means terrible lizard. There were dinosaurs with horns, dinosaurs with spikes, and dinosaurs with crests on their heads. Some walked on two legs and some walked on all four. Although true dinosaurs were neither fliers nor swimmers, some did float in the water. Some dinosaurs ate meat, and some were plant eaters. Most people think of the gigantic creatures that roamed the earth when they think of dinosaurs; however, some dinosaurs were very small. Dinosaur fossils have been found in all parts of the world.

1. The main idea of this story is...
   a. Dinosaurs came in all shapes and sizes.
   b. Some dinosaurs were meat-eaters.
   c. Most dinosaurs lived in North America.

2. This selection suggests that...
   a. Dinosaurs lived before there was written history.
   b. All dinosaurs were dangerous.
   c. Dinosaurs would not make good pets.

3. This selection suggests that...
   a. We know the exact cause of the dinosaurs' extinction.
   b. Fossils are easily found.
   c. Not all dinosaurs were huge creatures.

4. The best title for this story would be...
   a. Fossilized bones
   b. Fascinating Ancient Reptiles
   c. Reptiles and Amphibians

Interpreting: No. 12

Read the selection; then circle the letters which come before the correct answers.

Many different kind of trees grow in all parts of the world. Trees produce many kinds of foods, including fruits, nuts, olives, and spices. Rubber, cork, lumber, and paper are important non-food products of trees. Trees provide shade and shelter for various wildlife. They also produce oxygen. In addition, they are pleasing to see; parks and forests are popular recreational areas.

1. The main idea in this story is...
   a. Trees are prettiest in the fall.
   b. There are deciduous and coniferous trees.
   c. Trees provide humans with many useful products.

2. This selection suggests that...
   a. Trees are big plants.
   b. Trees are valuable to humans.
   c. Trees are destroyed by humans.

3. This selection suggests that...
   a. Many people like to visit the national parks and forests.
   b. Trees grow quickly.
   c. Rabbits like trees.

4. The best title for this story is...
   a. Trees Are Important
   b. Woodland Animals Are Numerous
   c. Trees Give Us Oxygen

Answers

Synonyms and Antonyms

SA-1

1. go
2. group
3. award
4. croaky
5. food
6. simple
7. small
8. look
9. threadbare
10. ring
11. certain
12. unusual
13. understood
14. purchase
15. learn
16. shocked
17. conceal
18. assist
19. student
20. limousine

SA-2

1. companion
2. ordinary
3. disappear
4. rational
5. disagree
6. question
7. sadness
8. sleepy
9. lessen
10. acquire
11. lazy
12. hold
13. gentle
14. single
15. tremble
16. scarce
17. present
18. edge
19. tell
20. disdain

SA-3

1. old
2. nose
3. mix
4. morning
5. good-hearted
6. firm
7. fair
8. care
9. competition
10. sly
11. thrifty
12. destroy
13. entertain
14. solitary
15. implant
16. change
17. bewilder
18. puzzle
19. concur
20. free

SA-4

1. stream
2. hidden
3. nearby
4. zone
5. caribou
6. jam
7. save
8. glide
9. maize
10. pure
11. physician
12. bravery
13. warning
14. magic
15. mild
16. moan
17. path
18. natural
19. tacky
20. extensive

SA-5

1. story
2. challenge
3. thread
4. reply
5. sharp
6. crimson
7. brisk
8. astonish
9. lumber
10. aloof
11. mature
12. choose
13. surplus
14. almost
15. threesome
16. void
17. cupboard
18. turf
19. splurge
20. terror

SA-6

1. misty
2. spicy
3. trip
4. speck
5. query
6. respond
7. clad
8. dilemma
9. guard
10. warm
11. peaceful
12. cold
13. meet
14. turn
15. clamor
16. mistake
17. transport
18. wonderful
19. vivid
20. saber

SA-7

1. slow
2. boy
3. heavy
4. floor
5. off
6. dirty
7. southwest
8. pull
9. close
10. walk
11. foot
12. aunt
13. inactive
14. straight
15. quiet
16. throw
17. increase
18. fact
19. reward
20. prevent

SA-8

1. normal
2. dirty
3. sad
4. old
5. day
6. after
7. last
8. laugh
9. bright
10. close
11. ashamed
12. nothing
13. low
14. short
15. narrow
16. rested
17. part
18. flexible
19. unbalanced
20. subtract

SA-9

1. timid
2. cheap
3. question
4. obscurity
5. waste
6. teacher
7. descend
8. ignorant
9. distant
10. lose
11. safety
12. drop
13. shrink
14. mellow
15. dry
16. rear
17. finish
18. old
19. beneath
20. weak

SA-10

1. advance
2. large
3. many
4. cold
5. fat
6. defeat
7. show
8. release
9. laconic
10. dry
11. graceful
12. polite
13. frown
14. stormy
15. tame
16. doubt
17. lend
18. generous
19. loud
20. sharp

SA-11

1. dull
2. easy
3. dry
4. succeed
5. sour
6. lie
7. shrink
8. dispose
9. scatter
10. healthy
11. cowardice
12. still
13. ignore
14. destroy
15. recent
16. bore
17. stand
18. deficit
19. sister
20. tight

SA-12

1. leave
2. start
3. obscure
4. criticize
5. continue
6. silence
7. unusual
8. ancient
9. foolish
10. new
11. lifesaving
12. center
13. bore
14. starve
15. comic
16. common
17. please
18. coolant
19. loser
20. menacing

Using Words Wisely

UW-1

1. sunny
2. then
3. but
4. gather
5. pentagon
6. inquisitive
7. love
8. gloomy
9. breeze
10. but
11. lexicon
12. attorney
13. extinction
14. flowers
15. dangerous
16. resented
17. contradict
18. dimmed
19. curator
20. frugal
21. minister
22. dormitories
23. sodden
24. mutiny

UW-2

1. discouraged
2. aggressive
3. paleontologist
4. manufacture
5. architect
6. articulate
7. petrified
8. whistling
9. crawl
10. excited
11. octagon
12. hutch
13. irritating
14. discards
15. stow
16. loft
17. importance
18. immaculately
19. playwright
20. pleasant
21. drenched
22. goblets
23. beverage
24. approaching

UW-3

1. ferry
2. armor
3. pharmacy
4. veterinarian
5. canine
6. paddled
7. cultivate
8. seek
9. tired
10. imaginary
11. drifted
12. impartial
13. suppress
14. insert
15. lances
16. monoplane
17. optimist
18. plantations
19. rapt
20. spacious
21. qualified
22. successful
23. expensive
24. boring

UW-4

1. syringe
2. brass
3. portrait
4. summary
5. hobbled
6. enclosed
7. secluded
8. patience
9. abundant
10. plead
11. respectful
12. reduction
13. dominated
14. energy
15. anecdote
16. challenge
17. cheerful
18. caravan
19. hazard
20. geologist
21. capacity
22. employer
23. courage
24. archery

UW-5

1. cozy
2. tinder
3. fossils
4. atlas
5. invertebrates
6. columns
7. spade
8. Orient
9. photosynthesis
10. calories
11. although
12. interpreter
13. math
14. condensed
15. prism
16. strong
17. appreciated
18. powerful
19. abbreviated
20. imagination
21. preparations
22. annoying
23. careful
24. source

UW-6

1. hobby
2. inhabitants
3. lizards
4. locating
5. characters
6. mixer
7. realized
8. rewarding
9. natural
10. affectionate
11. nutritious
12. eye
13. molar
14. addition
15. bravely
16. force
17. securely
18. sailboat
19. functioning
20. static
21. celebration
22. identified
23. blot
24. devastating

Determine the Meaning

DM-1

1. meeting
2. valuable
3. huge
4. country
5. covered
6. ended
7. lure
8. fake
9. flashy
10. camouflage
11. raised
12. breakable
13. secluded
14. accord

DM-2

1. businessman
2. active
3. strange
4. shows
5. rough
6. listen
7. odd
8. exhibit
9. wander
10. synthetic
11. real
12. gigantic
13. hole
14. accuse

DM-3

1. persuade
2. disturbance
3. mouth covering
4. serious
5. limbs
6. empty
7. frugal
8. druggist
9. prophecy
10. burning
11. front
12. antagonistic
13. rival
14. true

DM-4

1. positive
2. wary
3. lavish
4. miserly
5. restless
6. thoughtful
7. moisture
8. inactive
9. resident
10. customs
11. divided
12. needed
13. dreary
14. easy

DM-5

1. idea
2. grab
3. capture
4. glow
5. investigate
6. delicate
7. aim
8. structure
9. at least
10. excitedly
11. freezing
12. apron
13. weird
14. warm itself

DM-6

1. sure
2. copy
3. careless
4. rumors
5. reward
6. wheel guard
7. dangers
8. amusing
9. give
10. loss
11. postpone
12. far
13. silly
14. faithful

DM-7

1. shrinking
2. hot
3. important
4. sure
5. ocean
6. nervous
7. aims
8. pretend
9. unfinished
10. unlawful
11. strange
12. hid
13. enlarge
14. shrewd

DM-8

1. pull
2. scarf
3. sneaked
4. reach
5. teach
6. diary
7. method
8. many
9. visitor
10. unripened
11. ocean
12. dead
13. loudness
14. knowledgeable

DM-9

1. jealous
2. perfect
3. stale
4. strange
5. boring
6. worried
7. threatening
8. dangerous
9. difficult
10. slow
11. stirring
12. starved
13. confine
14. shake

DM-10

1. frightened
2. unusual
3. danger
4. peaceful
5. stop
6. leg
7. quickly
8. doctor
9. unknown
10. dependable
11. hunter
12. clogged
13. sometimes
14. decode

DM-11

1. clear
2. muscular
3. treasured
4. alike
5. duty
6. rival
7. lasting
8. former
9. meager
10. separate
11. gloomy
12. ridiculous
13. seclusion
14. uprising

SE-1

1. 3-5-1-2-4
2. 4-2-1-5-3
3. 3-4-1-5-2
4. 3-4-5-2-1

SE-2

1. 2-5-3-4-1
2. 4-3-2-1-5
3. 2-5-4-1-3
4. 2-1-3-4-5

SE-3

1. 4-2-1-3-5
2. 4-5-1-3-2
3. 5-4-1-2-3
4. 1-3-2-5-4

SE-4
1. 5-3-4-2-1
2. 3-1-4-2-5
3. 4-3-1-5-2
4. 5-1-4-3-2

SE-5
1. 1-4-2-5-3
2. 5-1-4-2-3
3. 5-2-1-3-4
4. 4-3-1-2-5

SE-6
1. 2-1-5-3-4
2. 1-4-2-5-3
3. 2-3-1-5-4
4. 2-3-1-4-5

Fact or Opinion

FO-1
1. F
2. O
3. F
4. F
5. F
6. O
7. F
8. F
9. O
10. O
11. F
12. F
13. F
14. F

FO-2
1. F
2. O
3. F
4. O
5. F
6. F
7. O
8. O
9. F
10. F
11. F
12. F
13. O
14. F

FO-3
1. O
2. F
3. F
4. O
5. F
6. F
7. F
8. O
9. F
10. F
11. F
12. F
13. O
14. O

FO-4
1. F
2. O
3. O
4. F
5. F
6. F
7. O
8. O
9. F
10. F
11. O
12. O
13. F
14. F

FO-5
1. O
2. F
3. F
4. F
5. F
6. F
7. F
8. O
9. F
10. F
11. O
12. F
13. O
14. O

FO-6
1. F
2. F
3. F
4. O
5. O
6. F
7. F
8. F
9. O
10. F
11. F
12. O
13. F
14. F

Interpreting

I-1
1. c
2. b
3. a
4. a

I-2
1. c
2. b
3. b
4. b

I-3
1. b
2. a
3. a
4. b

I-4
1. c
2. c
3. c
4. b

I-5
1. b
2. b
3. a
4. b

I-6
1. b
2. b
3. a
4. c

I-7
1. c
2. a
3. a
4. c

I-8
1. b
2. b
3. c
4. c

I-9
1. b
2. a
3. c
4. a

I-10
1. c
2. b
3. c
4. b

I-11
1. a
2. a
3. c
4. b

I-12
1. c
2. b
3. a
4. a